ROOTS OF WISDOM

Written by
Hong Yingming

Edited and illustrated by
Tsai Chih Chung

Translated by
Koh Kok Kiang

ASIAPAC • SINGAPORE

Publisher
ASIAPAC BOOKS PTE LTD
629 Aljunied Road #04-06
Cititech Industrial Building
Singapore 1438
Tel: 7453868
Fax: 7453822

First published January 1991
Reprinted November 1991, May 1992
            February 1993, March 1994

© ASIAPAC BOOKS, 1991
ISBN 9971-985-56-X

Typeset by Superskill Graphics Pte Ltd
Printed in Singapore by
Loi Printing Pte Ltd

Publisher's Note

Comics play an important role in our fast-moving urban society. They serve the young as well as the adult readers. Comics are not only fun and entertaining, they can also be a kind of satire. They can make classical literature and philosophy available to us in a light-hearted way.

The *Cai Gen Tan,* or *Roots of Wisdom,* is one of the gems of Chinese literature that sparkled briefly on the Chinese literary scene, then became forgotten. However in recent years, the book has found a new appeal among readers.

The *Roots of Wisdom* advocates a life of simplicity, goodness, quiet joy and harmony with one's fellow beings and the world at large. Hence it has great relevance to this modern and rapidly changing society of ours. Tsai Chih Chung has creatively illustrated about a third of the verses in the *Cai Gen Tan.*

We feel honoured to have the well-known cartoonist Tsai Chih Chung's permission to the translation right to his best selling comics. We would also like to take this opportunity to thank the translator and the typesetter for putting in their best efforts in the production of this series.

Asiapac's new corporate identity design

The Asiapac Books corporate symbol has its original inspiration from the Chinese character for Asia. The central globe symbolizes the international market for which we publish and distribute books, thereby helping to bridge the East and the West. The open book resembling soaring wings represents Asiapac, ever dynamic and innovative, aiming to communicate with modern society through the printed page. The green colour expresses Asiapac's commitment to go "green for life".

About the Editor/Illustrator

Tsai Chih Chung was born in 1948 in Chang Hwa County of Taiwan. He begun drawing cartoon strips at the age of 17. He worked as Art Director for Kuang Chi Programme Service in 1971. He founded the Far East Animation Production Company and the Dragon Cartoon Production Company in 1976, where he produced two cartoon films entitled *Old Master Q* and *Shao Lin Temple*.

Tsai Chih Chung first got his four-box comics published in newspapers and magazines in 1983. His funny comic characters such as the Drunken Swordsman, Fat Dragon, One-eyed Marshal and Bold Supersleuth have been serialized in newspapers in Singapore, Malaysia, Taiwan, Hong Kong, Japan, Europe, and the United States.

He was voted as one of the Ten Outstanding Young People in Taiwan in 1985. He has received wide acclaim from the media and the academic circle in Taiwan.

The comic book *Sayings of Zhuang Zi*, published in 1986, was a milestone in Tsai's career. Within two years, *Zhuang Zi* went into more than 72 reprints in Taiwan and 15 in Hong Kong and has to date sold over one million copies.

In 1987, Tsai Chih Chung published *Sayings of Lao Zi, Sayings of Confucius* and two books based on Zen. Since then, he has published more than 20 titles, out of which 10 are about ancient Chinese thinkers and the rest based on historical and literary classics. All these books topped the best sellers' list at one time or another. They have been translated into other languages such as Japanese, Korean, Thai, French, and Indonesian. Asiapac is the publisher for the English version of these comics.

Tsai Chih Chung can definitely be considered a pioneer in the art of visualizing Chinese literature and philosophy by way of comics.

Introduction

The *Cai Gen Tan* (literally, Vegetable Root Discourses), written during the twilight years of the Ming Dynasty (1368 – 1644), is one of the gems of Chinese literature.

It was briefly enjoyed after its publication, then forgotten as China became caught up in the throes of dynastic succession when the Manchus swept into Beijing and established the Qing Dynasty.

In recent years, there has been a resurgence of interest in the *Cai Gen Tan*, not only in the Chinese-speaking world, but also in East Asian societies such as Japan and South Korea.

This is not surprising as the contents of the *Cai Gen Tan* are applicable to every aspect of living. For instance, everyone wants to be happy, but the *Cai Gen Tan* says:

Happiness cannot be sought: nourish your own spirit of joy,
For this alone is the foundation for beckoning happiness.
Disaster cannot be avoided: flee from that which engenders the brutal,
For this alone is the way of keeping disaster at a distance.

In our dealings with others, we tend to be self-righteous. The *Cai Gen Tan* has this to say:

When attacking someone's faults, do not be too severe,
You need to consider how well he will weather what he hears,
When teaching someone by showing him what is good,
Do not pass certain heights, but hit upon what should be able to follow.

In essence, the *Cai Gen Tan* can be said to be a celebration of life:

People of this world put themselves in chains for the sake of gain and fame,
Then talk of the world of dust, the sea of bitterness.
They do not know that:
Clouds are white, mountains green.
Rivers run, rocks stand erect,
Blossoms invite, birds chirp merrily.
The valley responds, the woodcutters sing,
This world, again, is not of dust;
The sea, again, is not bitter,
It is only that, on their own, they put dust and bitterness in their hearts.

The writer of the book, Hong Yingming, was an obscure person about whom virtually nothing is known. This makes him as intriguing as Lao Zi, author of the Taoist classic *Dao De Jing*, whose existence is shrouded in the mists of time.

Hong, whose original name seems to have been Hong Zicheng, flourished around the late 16th Century. He receives no mention in Ming biographies or historical records and apart from the name, we know next to nothing about him.

From what we can learn about him in the book, we can surmise that he was a man of deep erudition, that he might possibly at one time have been a scholar-official, and that at the time he wrote the *Cai Gen Tan*, he may have been living as a recluse.

Hong had a remarkably profound education, as shown in his allusions to passages of Chinese literature and sayings of people ranging from poets to Zen monks. But instead of putting it to use for getting ahead in government or in business, he employed his learning to sharpen his perceptions and to give depth to his poetic and moral senses.

The book is in two parts, consisting of 357 verses altogether. It draws its material from the works of Confucianism, Taoism, Buddhism – the "three religions" of traditional China – and the poets and historians. The slim book is written in a poetic diction formed into parallel prose *(pian wen)*.

The book derives its title from a quote by the Song Dynasty philosopher Wang Xinmin: "If one is able to chew the vegetable greens and roots as well, he should be able to do all things."

This can be understood on two levels. First, if we do not chew things well, that is, if we do not ruminate or contemplate things over a period of time, we will never know their true taste or have a true understanding of them. This is what the Confucians called knowledge that "enters the ears and goes right out through the mouth".

Secondly, the image of the vegetable root is one of simplicity. If we are truly to live, it is the simple things in life that will give us life's true flavour.

Tsai Chih Chung has illustrated perhaps one-third of the verses in the *Cai Gen Tan*. This English edition, however, differs from Tsai's presentation of the *Cai Gen Tan* in that we have given the translation of the original verse written in classical Chinese instead of Tsai's interpretation in modern Chinese. This is to enable the English reader to have some idea of the poetic beauty of the original Chinese work.

At present, there is only one complete English translation of the *Cai Gen Tan*, entitled Roots of Wisdom. It is a competent work of scholarship by William Scott Wilsom (published in 1985 by Kodansha International).

Koh Kok Kiang

About the translator

Koh Kok Kiang is a journalist by vocation and a quietist by inclination. His interest in cultural topics and things of the mind started in his schooling years. It is his wish to discover the wisdom of the East that kindled his interest in Eastern philosophy. He has co-translated *Sayings of Lao Zi* and has also translated the following titles in Asiapac Comic Series: *Book of Zen, Origins of Zen, Sayings of Lao Zi Book 2, Sayings of Zhuang Zi Book 2, Thirty-six Stratagems.*

Contents

ROOTS OF WISDOM

The Man of True Wisdom

1 Strong wines and fatty meats, sweets and spicy foods – these do not have true taste.

2 True taste is only in the light and simple.

3 The mysterious and the strange, the pre-eminent and the uncommon – these are not men with true wisdom.

4 The man with true wisdom is only the ordinary man.

Fascinating and novel things do not endure. That which endures is the plain and ordinary. Anything that is contrived loses its natural flavour. Only that which is natural is true.

Natural Quietude

1
Heaven and earth remain peacefully unmoved, Yet their life-breath is unceasing, and is seldom known to rest.

The sun and the moon hasten through their courses day and night, Yet their befitting light has not changed through the ages.
2

Thus for the gentleman: It is necessary during times of leisure to keep in mind what is proper for emergencies.
3

4
It is necessary during times of hastening to retain an element of composure.

Man has to follow the natural course and act according to circumstances. One's heart will then be unruffled in the face of challenges and changes.

The Clear Mind

1 Of those who make their meals from simple herbs and vegetables,

2 Many are as pure as ice, as stainless as gems.

3 Those who dress in fancy clothes and feast sumptuously,

4 Lower themselves to acting like servants and slaves.

5 Ultimately the mind is made clear by simplicity.

6 And integrity lost by opulence.

One who does not seek favours from others is naturally upright. The person who is content with plain fare will be unmoved by temptations.

Helping Others, Helping Oneself

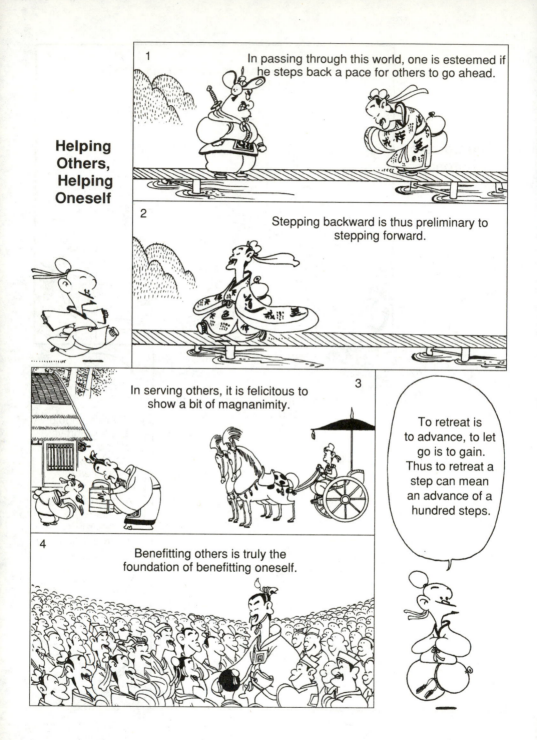

1. In passing through this world, one is esteemed if he steps back a pace for others to go ahead.

2. Stepping backward is thus preliminary to stepping forward.

3. In serving others, it is felicitous to show a bit of magnanimity.

To retreat is to advance, to let go is to gain. Thus to retreat a step can mean an advance of a hundred steps.

4. Benefitting others is truly the foundation of benefitting oneself.

Right Action

1 Even if one has performed world-shaking meritorious deeds,

2 If their value is not to be negated, the word "pride" does not apply.

3 Even if one has committed a crime that has reached the heavens,

4 If one has truly repented, the word "regret" does not apply.

One who thinks he is all-powerful courts disasters. Even if one commits the worst atrocity, so long as he deeply repents, the offence will fade into nothingness.

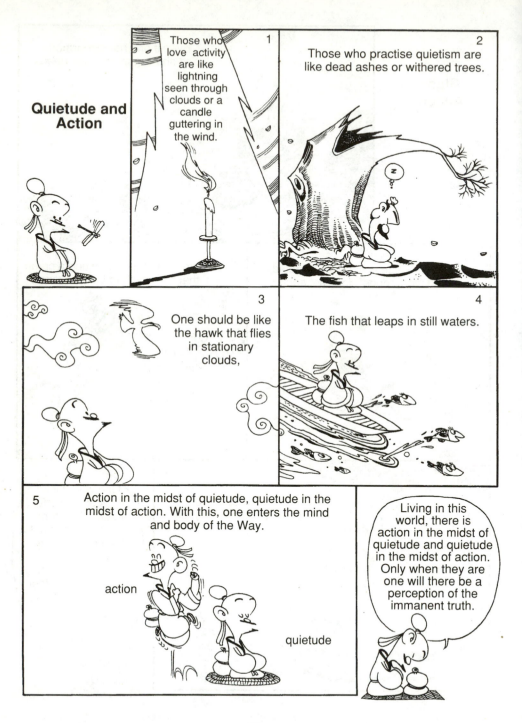

Quietude and Action

1. Those who love activity are like lightning seen through clouds or a candle guttering in the wind.

2. Those who practise quietism are like dead ashes or withered trees.

3. One should be like the hawk that flies in stationary clouds,

4. The fish that leaps in still waters.

5. Action in the midst of quietude, quietude in the midst of action. With this, one enters the mind and body of the Way.

action

quietude

Living in this world, there is action in the midst of quietude and quietude in the midst of action. Only when they are one will there be a perception of the immanent truth.

Not to Forsake Anything

1. When outfitted in the robes of a high official,

2. One should not forsake the savour of the mountain recluse.

3. When living among the forests and the springs,

4. One should preserve in his heart the administration of the state.

One who holds high office must have an unsullied reputation to win the respect and admiration of the people. The ordinary citizen will then show an interest in affairs of the state and play their part for the good of the nation.

Burden and Ease

1. To be overly concerned about one's duties is a kind of virtue.

2. But to bring oneself too much hardship because of them is neither fitting to one's constitution nor felicitous to human nature.

3. To revere simplicity and be unattached is indeed an indication of high character,

4. But to maintain too much elegant simplicity is neither helpful to humanity nor useful to the world at large.

One's conduct in the world must be objective and impartial. Good fortune and happiness will then smile on one.

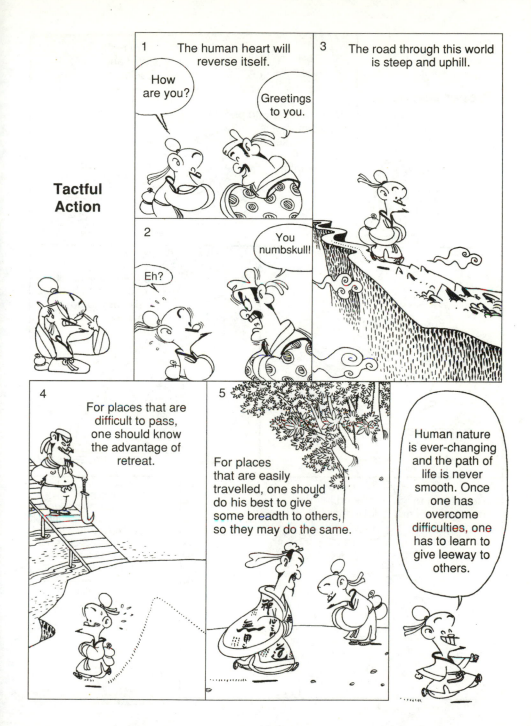

Tactful Action

Proper Behaviour

The Free Spirit

1
If others possess wealth, then I possess humanity.

Wealth
Humanity

2
If others possess high status, then I possess justice.

Status
Justice

3
Therefore the gentleman never inveigles his government.

4
If men would be established in goodness, they could gain mastery of heaven.
If they gathered their energy, they would have command of their life-force.

5
The gentleman does not accept the shackles of the created world.

A gentleman of calibre treats people with love and humanity and acts in accordance with what is right. He will not let others influence him but establish his own foundation for living. Why allow oneself to be trapped by fame and wealth?

Doing Things in the Right Spirit

1

For the person who would study, it is necessary to collect one's spirit and to apply oneself in earnest.

2

But if in cultivating virtue there remains any idea of merit or fame, learning will invariably amount to nothing.

3

Spring has varied blooms, Autumn its resplendent moon, Summer its soothing breeze, Winter its carpet of snow...

And if in reading books there is a tendency towards recitation and stylishness,

4

Surely there will be nothing in the depths of the heart.

The purpose of acquiring knowledge is to nourish one's character. But one who merely pursues knowledge as an end in itself misses the point of education.

Desire that Clouds the Mind

1. Everybody has the capacity for great benevolence. The mind of the Bodhisattva Vimalakirti is not different from that of a butcher or executioner.

2. All places have the capacity for true enjoyment. A house made from the finest materials is not different from a hut with thatched eaves.

3. Ah, but desire covers up and longings envelope,

4. And that which is right in front of you becomes mixed and mistaken Causing the tiniest part of an inch to become a thousand miles.

Man's nature is basically good but it is often clouded by desires. It is like a person who suddenly loses his sight. Isn't this lamentable?

The Big-hearted Man

1 One should not keep in mind the services he has rendered to others.

2 Nor should he forget the troubles he has caused.

3 One should not forget the favours others have done for him,

Nor should he harbour feelings of enmity.

Wholeness

When the water vessel is full, it overturns.

1

While the piggy bank remains empty, it is whole.

2

3

Therefore the gentleman:
Resides in vacuity rather than existence.

4

And exists in the lacking rather than the saturation.

When taut, the bow cannot be stretched further. When full, the moon cannot be any brighter. The gentleman who does not go beyond the limit knows contentment. He is not far from the Way.

Peace of Mind

1

Men know the happiness of fame and position.

They do not know that obscurity and lack of position is the happiness of the highest truth.

2

3

Men know the affliction of hunger and cold.

4

They do not know that the perpetual insecurity of the rich is an affliction more excessive still.

There is no definite good or bad about the things of the world. It all depends on how one looks at them.

Aimless Existence

1

The restive horse that has overturned the carriage can, at last, be made to run properly.

2

The melting metal that leaps out of the mould can, in the end, be returned to the cast.

3

But the man who lives only in peaceful amusement without rousing himself to action will, until the end of his life, make no progress at all.

Gosh! Don't fritter away your life any more.

Philosopher Chen Baisha (1428-1499) of the Ming Dynasty said:

There are many afflictions involved in becoming a man, but none are sufficient to make him hide his face in shame. I lament only the man who lives his life without any afflictions at all.

4

5

This is truly a solid argument.

One should not fear having faults and shortcomings. What is worse is to know of one's faults and yet not do anything about them.

The Folly of Greed

To Be One's Own Master

1 Ears, eyes, seeing and hearing – these are thieves of the external.

2 Emotion, desire and consciousness of self – these are thieves of the internal.

3 Only when the man who is his own master,

The heart that is naturally pure.

4 Sits alone within the temple,

5 Will the thieves be transformed into servants of the House.

Ears
Eyes
Body
Nose
Will
Mouth
Tongue

Temptations from the outside can cause one to lose one's head while one's own greed can cause one to sink into folly. One must be on the guard at all times to preserve purity of nature.

Mindfulness

1

Instead of making plans for work that has not yet been completed.

2

One should preserve the projects that have already been achieved.

3

Instead of regretting the mistakes of the past.

4

One should hold in check his lapses of the future.

One has to have a steadfast character and act accordingly. Where there are setbacks, one must learn from one's mistakes and not wallow in regret.

The Silent Mind

1. The wind soughs through the bamboo, And when it has passed, the bamboo has no sound.

2. The goose flies over the cold clear pool, And when it has gone, the pool retains no image.

3. Therefore, for the gentleman, a thing is manifest when it appears for the first time in his mind.

4.

5. When the thing has ceased, his mind commits itself to the void.

People often feel anxiety and apprehension over things yet to happen and regret over things past. Thus do people pass their days in sorrow and pain.

True Enjoyment

1. The peace that comes from peaceful surroundings is not true peace:

2. Only in the peace obtained in the midst of activity is found the true sphere of one's original nature.

3. The pleasure that comes from pleasurable surroundings is not true enjoyment:

4. Only with the joy obtained in the midst of suffering can one see the true movements of the mind.

A person usually has a change of heart when circumstances are favourable. To be able to go beyond the influence of circumstances is to know the real essence of the heart.

Superior and Inferior Deeds

1. If a common person ventures to cultivate virtue or perform a good deed,

2. Your compassion is like that of a bodhisattva.
   It is just like being a high official, but without rank.

3. If a man of high rank recklessly flaunts his power or markets his patronage,
   Your Majesty is indeed farsighted. Your brilliance is peerless.

4. He becomes, in the end, only a titled beggar.
   You may have this official post.
   Thank you, Your Majesty, for your wise decision.

A person's calibre has nothing to do with high or low status, but whether or not there is integrity. High officials who are sycophantic towards superiors – aren't they no better than beggars?

The
Right Touch

When literature is composed at its best, there is nothing particularly extraordinary about it: it is simply appropriate.

1

This is so well-written: not a character too many nor one too little.

Marvellous!

Excellent!

3 When human character is developed at its best, there is nothing particularly wonderful about it: it is simply natural.

2

His character is perfect.

4

When doing things, one should act with natural ease without the slightest compulsion. Acting with too much strain generally does not have a favourable outcome.

The
Transiency
of Life

Heaven and earth exist for ten thousand ages, but this body you will not receive again.

1

Man's life spans no more than a hundred years, but the days pass with the greatest of ease.

2

He who has the good fortune to be born should not be unknowing of the joy of living,

3

Nor should he be oblivious of the sorrow of life's vanity.

4

Heaven and earth endures but human life is limited. As a human being, one must appreciate the wonders and meaning of life. Only then will life not be wasted.

The Root of Sorrow

The diseases of old age are all incurred at the time of our youth.

1

The adversities that overtake us after we start to decline were all created at the time of our prosperity.

2

3

Therefore, when the gentleman is enjoying status and fortune,

4

He is extremely apprehensive.

When a gentleman has title and fortune, he should watch his sayings and doings. When young, one should take care of the body so that it will last a lifetime without being worn out.

The Right
Way to
Respond

1

When encountering a
gentleman of deep reticence,
do not for a moment
communicate your true mind.

2

When seeing a man of high-
strung self-satisfaction,
do your best to keep him from
opening his mouth.

Those who
are taciturn
are generally
scheming and
devious, keeping
things under
wraps. Those
who are full of
conceit are aloof
and deaf to the
words of others.

Keeping Out of Harm's Way

1
How are you?

Greetings to you!

Though you are aware of the deceit of others, do not let this appear in words.

2
Though you receive the contempt of others, do not let this move your temper.

Between the two of these there is an infinity of meaning. Between the two of these there is an infinity of use.

When bullied and wronged by others, one should remain unruffled. If one observes the situation but does not react, then chances are that one will be unharmed.

3

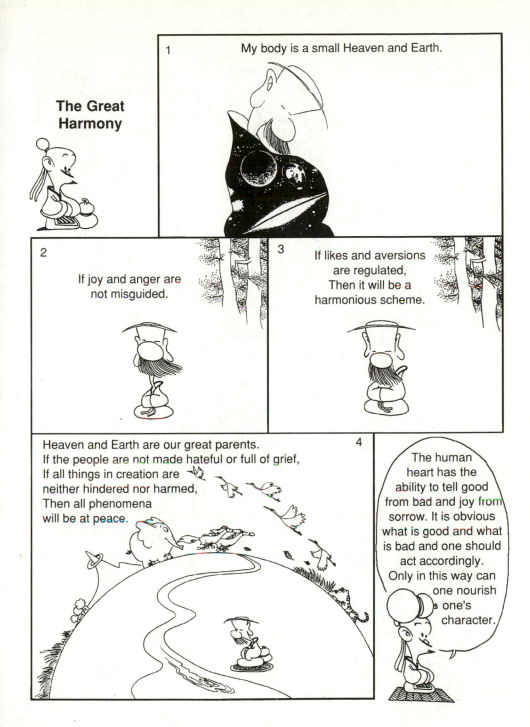

The Great Harmony

1 My body is a small Heaven and Earth.

2 If joy and anger are not misguided.

3 If likes and aversions are regulated, Then it will be a harmonious scheme.

4 Heaven and Earth are our great parents. If the people are not made hateful or full of grief, If all things in creation are neither hindered nor harmed, Then all phenomena will be at peace.

The human heart has the ability to tell good from bad and joy from sorrow. It is obvious what is good and what is bad and one should act accordingly. Only in this way can one nourish one's character.

40

Allow Others an Escape Route

1. In weeding out scoundrels or cutting off flatterers, it is necessary to leave them a means of escape.

Leave the money behind. You will have a chance to live. Just go.

2. If you deal with them but allow no way out,

No way out for you. I am going to eliminate evil. Don't try to escape.

You're too much. Let us perish together!

Revolt! Revolt!

3.

4. It is like stopping up the hole of a mouse.

5. You no longer have any means of escape.

6. When all means of escape have been totally blocked, It will chew its way through all your valuables.

Rebellion! Rebellion!

In dealing with wrongdoers, one must not be too harsh. If one does not give them a chance to repent but drives them into desperation, this will only result in tragedy.

43

Character Defects

1. When hungry, they stick to you.

2. When full, they fly away like the wind.

3. If there is wealth, they trot right over,

4. Where there is poverty, they abandon.

These are the common defects of human character.

People often change their attitudes towards others because of changes in their fortunes and circumstances. This is a common fault of humans.

44

Composure of the Gentleman

1 The gentleman should cleanse and purify his vision,

2 Grrr...

This is really too much!

3

4 How wicked you people are! You've really gone too far!

5 You are not satisfied with our behaviour?

How dare you take sides!

But, with respect, not stand thoughtlessly obstinate in his views.

In one's dealings with the world, one should be calm, careful and circumspect. Only if one does not appear to be self-righteous will he not bring disaster upon himself.

The Wisdom of Solitude

When the single flame flickers like fireflies, and the music of all creation is suspended, I enter, for the first time, a peaceful solitude.

1

When first waking from the dreams of dawn, and the bustling of the crowds has not yet begun, I leave, for the first time, the chaos of pre-creation.

2

Riding these moments, if I ponder and meditate, letting wisdom shine and glow.

3

I know for the first time: my ears, eyes, mouth and nose are all shackles,

Eyes

Ears

Nose

Mouth

4

Emotions, desires, tastes and predilections are but tricks and schemes.

5

Just before one goes to sleep and just after waking up is generally when the mind is most clear. The benefit is greatest when such times are used for contemplation.

46

Preserving One's Integrity

1

When resigning from an office, you should resign at the height of your strength.

When finding a place for yourself, you should look for a place where you can be alone.

When something is accomplished, leave no trace of your role. This will prevent future problems. If one does not contend for fame and power, does not seek to prove one's ability, then one will not invite the wrath and jealousy of others.

2

49

Earthiness

1

Rather than associating with sophisticated city people, make friends with the humble old folks who live in the mountains.

2

Rather than having audiences in opulent residences, become intimate with those who live in thatched huts.

Rather than listening in on the talk of streets and ports, let your ears be filled with the songs of woodcutters and cowherds.

3

Rather than talking about your contemporaries' vices and blunders, relate the fine sayings and actions of the men of old.

4

Rather than consort with the rich and powerful, it is better to associate with ordinary commoners. To listen to gossip is not as good as listening to words of truth. To discuss the imperfections of others is not as good as to mention the good deeds of the ancients. Instead of veering towards wickedness, it is far better to approach goodness.

Foundation of Goodness

1

Character is the foundation of achievement.

2

Where the foundation is not secure, there is yet to be a structure firm and long-lasting.

To perform an undertaking, one must have the foundation to make it possible. If the foundation is not sound, things will not endure. Magnanimity and goodness can be said to be the foundation for any undertaking.

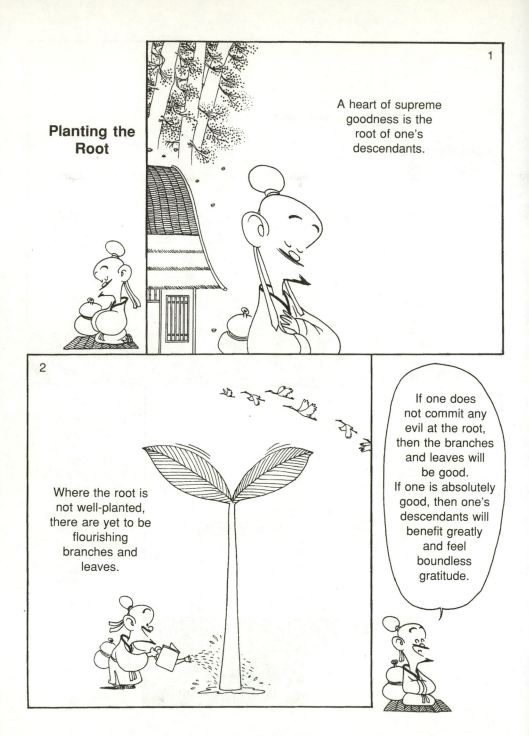

Planting the Root

1

A heart of supreme goodness is the root of one's descendants.

2

Where the root is not well-planted, there are yet to be flourishing branches and leaves.

If one does not commit any evil at the root, then the branches and leaves will be good. If one is absolutely good, then one's descendants will benefit greatly and feel boundless gratitude.

Non-attachment

Philosopher Wang Yangming (1472-1528) of the Ming Dynasty said:

Do not throw away your own inexhaustible storehouse and imitate the indigents who hold their bowls and line the gates.

1

2

It is also said:

The rich with indigent souls! Rest from your preaching of dreams! Will fire from the stove of any house not make the smoke rise?

One verse warns against being blind to one's own possessions.

3

The other remonstrates against pride in what one owns.

4

Both can be important precepts for the student.

Everything is of equal value in existence. There is no need to compare and to feel inadequacy nor to feel abundance and brag about it.

Sustenance for All

1

The Way is one kind of public domain.

2

It should be encouraged to everyone.

3

Learning is a sort of daily meal.

4

When I see something good, I learn from it. When I see something bad, I avoid doing it.

It should be strongly recommended to all.

Knowledge is something anyone can acquire. As long as one is determined to learn, there are no limits to knowledge.

Oneself and Others

55

Human-heartedness

1

"For the sake of the mice, they always left out rice."

2

"In pity for the moths, they did not light the candles."

3

Thoughts like these of the people of old are the agencies that help us to flourish as human beings.

4

Without them we are no better than bodies of earth and wood.

A compassionate nature is inherent in sentient beings. All good deeds spring from compassion. One who does not have compassion is no better than an empty shell of a body.

Official and Domestic Conduct

1

When working in an official capacity, there are two words of advice. It is said: "If only there is impartiality, clarity will grow."

2

"If only there is honesty, authority will grow."

When residing at home, there are two words of advice. It is said:

If only there is sympathy, emotions will be at peace.

3

If only there is thrift, what is used will be sufficient.

4

A good official who is impartial wins the respect and admiration of others. A good householder who is mild-mannered ensures happiness and peace in the family.

Breadth
of
Vision

Let
Things
Be

1
Give up confronting petty people;

2
Petty people will, of themselves, confront each other.

3
Give up fawning upon men of high quality;

4
Men of high quality are, from the beginning, without self-interest.

Contending with petty people will only invite more troubles. Being sycophantic towards a gentleman will only earn his disdain.

60

Press On!

1

Do not be distressed when events run counter to your wishes.

Do not be overjoyed when things go your way.

Heh, heh! I have acquired a fat fortune.

2

3

Do not count on prolonged contentment.

4

Do not shy away from initial difficulties.

One must act with resolve and determination and not because of a moment's comfort slacken in one's efforts. Only then will he make progress.

Keeping Cool

1 The cool eye discerns men's character.

2 The cool ear hears the intent of their speech.

3 Cool emotions plumb others' feelings.

4 The cool mind penetrates everything.

Human beings tend to be easily excitable. In handling affairs, one has to observe the situation comprehensively and calmly. And when acting thus with reason, one will not fall into error.

Circumspection

The Man of True Worth

1. When the gentleman suffers difficulties, he is not distressed.

2. But finding himself at the banquet seat, he shrinks back in uneasiness.

3. When meeting a man of influence and power, he does not miss a beat.

4. But to encounter the distressed and lonely unsettles his mind.

A gentleman remains unruffled by sudden changes in fortune. He is steadfast and does not give in to temptations. When a gentleman sees others in distress, he does not take advantage of the situation for his own benefit.

ROOTS OF WISDOM —
PART TWO

Transcendence

Listening to the sound of the bell
in the peaceful night,
I am called into sobriety from my
dream within a dream.

Watching the reflection of the
moon in the clear deep pool,
I get a glimpse of the body
beyond this earthly shell.

When listening to the sound of a bell in the dead of night, there is peace in the heart and the mind becomes clearer. One who is usually befuddled will then have a moment of clarity.

75

The Essence of Things

1 People understand how to read books that have words,

2 But do not understand how to read those that lack them.

To the man of wisdom, there is the unwritten book of mountains and rivers, and the book of flowers and the moon.

3 They know how to pluck the lute that has strings,

4 But do not know how to pluck the one that has none.

To the man who is wise, the music of nature is everywhere.

Caught by the form but untouched by the spirit: How will they get at the substance of either music or literature?

5 When looking or listening with all of one's being, one discovers books without words, music without tunes.

The Uncon-taminated Heart

1

If the heart contains no worldly desires,

2

You will have autumnal skies and cloudless seas.

3

If you can sit with just a lute and a book,

4

Wherever you are becomes the realm of sages.

When the heart has no desires, everywhere is paradise. When leading a life of simplicity, one knows true joy and beauty of things.

Total Insight

1

When you have grasped the essence of a single thing,

2

The mists and moon of the Five Lakes* will be within your heart.

3

When you have broken through the secrets right before your eyes, One thousand heroes of old will be delivered to your grasp.

"A world in a grain of sand." If one can understand this, then there is no difference between a grain of sand and lakes or mountains. Thus one will understand the meaning of the ancients.

* Famous scenic places in China.

78

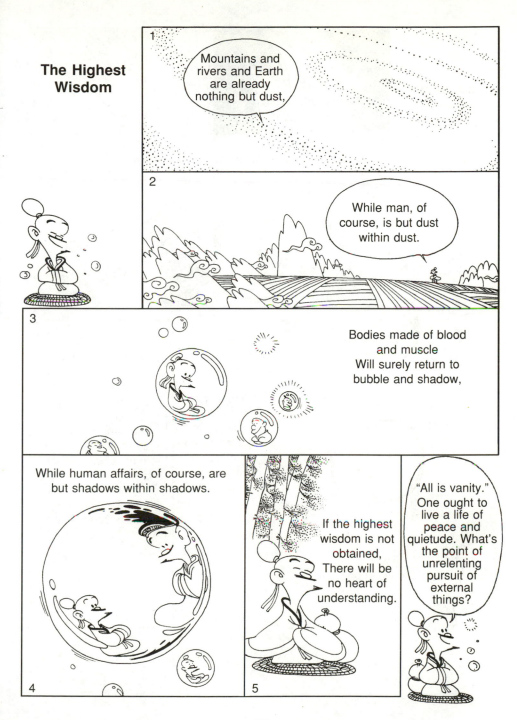

The Highest Wisdom

Inconsequential Things

Within the light of the flint's spark, they fight over "long" and compete over "short."

My disposition is more admirable than yours!

My talent is greater than yours!

Yet how much time can there be?

Rubbish!

I've won!

1

2

I am the real victor.

It is I who is stronger.

Above the horns of the tiny snail, they compare their losses and argue about gains.

The Earth is but a speck of dust in the immensity of the universe and human lifespan is but a moment in time. In the brief lifespan of ours, cherish what is truly beautiful and do not waste it on contending over inconsequential things.

3

Yet how big can the world be?

Hee! Hee!

4

Tranquil Moments

1
In a valley of pines, I walk alone with staff in hand;

2
Standing still for a moment, clouds rise around my tattered robes.

3
Beneath a window looking out on bamboos, I stretch out with a book for my pillow.

4
When I awake, the moon shines in on the cold cracked floor.

"The clouds are my friends; the wind and the moon my family." This kind of beautiful feeling is not dependent on any conditions. Anyone can come upon it.

Man who can Abide Anywhere

1

He who has a taste for quietism
Looks into the white clouds and hazy crags and becomes intimate with the mysterious.

2

He who runs after the magnificent
Watches sublime dances and listens to beautiful songs and forgets all fatigue.

This place is fine.

3

Only for the man who is satisfied with himself is there neither tumult nor quiet,
Neither the magnificent nor the withered.
There is no place he can go that is not appropriate for him.

One who perceives the truth about things acts naturally and is not bothered by surroundings. He is free everywhere.

This place is also just as good.

Free and Easy

A single cloud
leaves the peak:
Going or staying –
it is in no place
involved.

1

2

A bright mirror moon
hangs in the sky:
Peace or noise – with
neither is it concerned.

If one is
influenced by
external
things, he
cannot move
freely. If one
is not subject
to external
influences, he
can act freely.

Emptiness of Phenomena

The water flows, but no turbulence is there:

From this one learns the meaning of seeing peace in the midst of tumult.

The mountains are high, but the clouds are unobstructed:

From this one awakes to the chance of passing from existence to non-existence.

If the mind is silent, it is completely uninfluenced by anything and yet it is part of everything. The individual is then one with everything and there is the state of no-self.

Contaminated mind

1
Mountains and forests are excellent places.
But once you put designs on them, they become no better than the marketplace.

2
Books and paintings are elegant things.
But once they are coveted unreasonably, they become no better than pawned goods.

3
Generally, if the mind is untainted,
Even the vulgar world is the realm of sages.

4
But if the mind is infatuated,
Even places of pleasure become seas of regret.

If the heart is uncontaminated, everywhere is a good place.

Man of Freedom

1
On the reed mat, I lie down amidst the snow, sleep above the clouds,

2
And, in the single room, am able to preserve The refreshing force of the night's serenity.

3
Well into my cup I chant into the wind, Play under the moon,

4
And am able to take this body and hide it away, ten thousand leagues from the world's crimson dust.

Nature has many wonders. If one interacts with Nature sufficiently, then this will elevate one's spirits.

Peace is Everywhere

Walking beneath the bamboo hedge,
When I suddenly hear a dog bark, a cock crow,
It vaguely seems as though I'm in a world
amidst the clouds.

Sitting in my book-lined room,
When I listen intently to the cicada's cry, the crow's noisy caw,
For the first time I know the universe of peace.

When the mind is one with everything, all sounds are peaceful sounds.

Nothing to Worry About

If I do not seek prosperity,

Why should I be troubled by the sweet-smelling bait of profit or reward?

If I do not compete to get ahead, Why should I fear the inevitable danger of working for the state?

If one maintains purity of heart all the time, then one need not worry about temptations from others.

Putting the House in Order

Rambling among the mountains and forests, springs and rocks, The mind soiled by the dust of the world gradually expires.

1

2

Playing leisurely with poetry and books, paintings and sketches, The spirit of the vulgar quietly ceases.

Therefore the gentleman: Does not take pleasure in material things and lose his free will;

3

He makes use of another land and regulates his mind.

Beautiful scenery can soothe the restless heart. Literature and painting can uplift the spirit.

4

Purity of Mind and Body

1

Spring days have an air of prosperity and bustle, And this makes men's mind expansive and at ease,

2

But this is not equal to the days of autumn When clouds are white and the winds are pure, Orchids fragrant and the cassia sweet-smelling,

3

The moon shines vacuous and bright above, and is reflected the same below, And this makes men pure in both body and mind.

The freshness of spring cannot be compared with the mellowness of autumn. If one lives with gay abandon while young, when he is old it will be too late to recover lost innocence and purity of mind.

The Essence of Things

He who does not know a single Chinese character, But who possesses the true meaning of poetry, Has obtained poetry's true substance.

On a spring day's moonlit night, the patter of raindrops and the croaking of frogs are in harmony.

1

He who has not recited a single gatha, But who possesses the taste of Zen, Is awake to the mysteries of its teachings.

You bring enlightenment to people, I also bring enlightenment to the statue.

To know words and to study Zen gathas is like book learning. It is merely building up knowledge of Zen. Perception has nothing to do with learning.

2

The Restless and the Calm

1

He whose nerves are agitated Will look at the shadow of a bow and suspect it of being a snake or scorpion,

2

Will look at stationary rocks and imagine them to be tigers in waiting. In this frame of mind, everything contains a mortal danger.

3

He whose thoughts have been suspended Can make violent men as gentle as sea gulls,

4

Can equate the voice of the frog with the sound of the drum and the flute. In everything he touches, he sees the functions of truth.

If the mind is not quiet, when the wind blows and the grass moves, one becomes agitated. If there is silence of the mind, nothing can un-settle it.

Body and Mind

1

The body is like an unmoored boat: Whether it proceeds or is thwarted is only up to the current.

2

The mind resembles a dried-up tree:

3

How can it be moved by the cleaving of swords or the coating of cosmetics?

He's very bad.

He's beyond hope.

He's a remarkable person.

He looks refined.

"Success and failure cannot move me and affect my peace of mind and steadfastness." Only when this is so can one know absolute freedom and joy.

Desire and Absence of Desire

1
He who is filled with desire
Is like the waves that seethe
over the cold abyss:

2
Even in mountains
and forests he does
not see peace.

How boring!

3
He who is filled
with vacuity
Is like the cool
breeze born from
intense heat:

Easy does it.

4
Even within town and market he
does not know noise.

If the mind is quiet and unruffled, and no desire is stirred up, though one lives in a bustling metropolis, he is at ease always. Even if the highest praise is heaped upon him, he is unmoved.

Reaction

Gu De, a Zen monk of the Tang Dynasty, said: "The shadow of the bamboo sweeps the steps, but the dust is unmoved."

"The reflection of the moon makes its way through the pond, but in water there is no trace."

Shao Yaofu, a Confucian scholar of the Northern Song Dynasty, said: "Though the waters flow rapidly, the area is always serene."

"Though the flowers fall incessantly, the mind is of itself at peace."

If men would always maintain these thoughts, And with them react to events, encounter external things, How free their bodies and minds would be.

The gentleman should act according to circumstances. When something needs to be done, one has to do it whole-heartedly and when it is over, one need not gloat over it. Only in this way can original nature be untainted.

Changing Fortunes

1
Foxes sleep on the broken paving stones.

2
Rabbits run through the deserted tower.

3
Here was, in years long past, a place of dances and songs.
The dew chills the chrysanthemums,
The mists become lost in the dried-up grass;
Everything here, in times long ago, was witness to war.

4
Prosperity and decline, how can either continue?
Strength and weakness, can either exist for long?
Thinking of this, man's heart turns to ashes.

Gain or loss is an endless cycle; power and weakness are just human concepts. Wealth and honour is as empty as a dream. If one can understand this, then he would not become a slave to his desires and get ensnared by things.

Unperturbed Heart

103

Types of People

1. Under a clear sky and bright moon, How many should be flitting free under the heavens:

2. The flitting moths that alone throw themselves into the night lights?

3. With a clear spring and green grasses, How many things should they be able to peck at and eat:

4. The owls that so love the rotted flesh of mice?

5. Ah, those people in this world who do not resemble the moths and owls, How many can there be?

Life is like the boundless sea and sky that allows people to move freely, except that people put themselves in confinement. In pursuing status and wealth, they court their own doom like the moths which are drawn to the bright lights.

Ignorance

1

When one has finally got onto the raft,
to then think about abandoning it:
This is surely an unobstructed
Man of the Way.

2

To be already riding
the donkey, and then
go out in search of it:
This is, in the end, the
Zen Master of no
enlightenment.

? ?

A boat is
just a means to
reach a place.
When one gets to
the destination,
the boat can be
forgotten. Man is
complete in
himself but in the
quest for Truth,
the more one
pursues it, the
further one
strays
from it.

Not This and Not That

The True Void is not Void.

1

2

What's that?

Attachment to phenomena is not Truth.

Waves.

Wrong! Not waves but water.

3

4

But breaking through phenomena is also not Truth.

107

5 You ask, what did the Buddha say about this?

6 "Exist in the world, but transcend it."

7 Following one's desires is bitterness.

8 But suppressing one's desires is also bitterness.

9 This is what follows naturally from all our disciplines.

To be caught in duality and delusion is to be at odds with the truth of things. To involve oneself in secular affairs and yet not be bound by them is the most transcendent way of mundane living.

Shallowness of Things

1. When one has had enough of the world's taste, He accepts that human emotions change from rain to clouds with the turn of a hand,

   Your help is indispensable. I need you to do something for me.

2. And laments at even opening his eyes.

   I don't need you any more. Get lost!

3. When one has understood the nature of man,

   You're a good person.

   Oh yes?

4. He lets himself be called a cow or a horse, And simply nods his head in assent.

   You're a useless bum!

   Really?

   Once a man has tasted the full range of human emotions, he will see through everything. He accepts that humans are capricious and even when things are at their lowest point, he will not sink into despair.

Peace and Confusion

1
If one's original nature is clear, Though he eats when hungry and drinks when thirsty, He will not be without peace and relaxation for body and mind.

What is Zen?

When hungry, eat; when tired, sleep.

2
If one's mind has become sunken and confused,

3
Though he expounds Zen doctrine and chants the gathas,

The sound of the valley is like one long note, but the colours of the mountains are not of one body.

4
The more I read, the more I do not understand.

All will be playing and trifling with both spirit and soul.

One cannot hope to have clarity when the mind is confused to begin with. If one practises Zen in such a state of mind, then one's efforts will be futile.

Mundane Ties

1 Gold is taken from ore;

2 Gems are produced from rock.

3 Without illusion, there would be no seeking after Truth. The Way may be obtained within one's cups.

4 The land of enchantment seen in the midst of revelry.

Although refinement exists, we cannot part from the mundane. If one is steeped in worldly affairs, he cannot but be trapped by the secular world. The thing to do is to live in the mundane world but transcend it.

The Beauty of Simplicity

1 If the spirit is fully in bloom, Though one inhabits a room wearing only rough clothes,

2 He will obtain the harmonious energy of the universe.

3 If what one tastes is satisfactory, Though he eats only plain fare,

4 He will know the true taste of human simplicity.

Though things may be at their lowest point, one can still derive the greatest joy from living. This is possible when one has reached the stage when no one can make him do what at heart he does not want to do.

Expansive Mind

1
If, in a place as small as a shed,
One tosses away all his myriad thoughts,

2
Will he not enjoy the clouds that pass by painted eaves
And the rain that falls by the jewelled bound blind?

3
If, after three cups of wine,
The Truth of Oneness is, of itself, obtained,

4
One will know perfectly how to play an unadorned lute under the moon,

5
Or the short flute into the wind.

If one can drop the burdens of thought, then he will be able to appreciate the full flavour of life.

Letting Go and Holding Fast

1. One should let go of body and mind, and entrust things unseen to the workings of Nature.

Tang Dynasty poet Bai Juyi said:

2. Song Dynasty poet Zhao Buzhi said:

One should discipline body and mind, and return them encased to peace and regulation.

3. Letting go too far results in excess and insanity,

4. But too much discipline leads to dessication.

5. Only he who directs body and mind well holds the hilt of the sword and leaves discipline and its lack to be on their own.

To be utterly indifferent to affairs and to be overly concerned about things are both not right. If one can see the underlying truth of things, then he can go beyond mundane wisdom.

Vainglory

1

The actress puts on white powder
and daubs herself with rouge,
And with the tip of the brush creates
both beauty and crone.

2

But when the songs have been sung
and the theatre is closed,
Where are beauty and crone then?

3

The chess player
fights for the fore
and contends
for the rear,
Competes with
each stone for victory
or defeat.

Attack!

Gosh!

4

But when the game
has ended and the
stones are put away,
Where are victory
and defeat then?

When performing on stage, the actor has an air of pride and dignity. When the show is over, he is but someone who works for a living. He may be good at acting, but when the performance is over, he is just an ordinary person living in the world.

116

All in the Mind

1

Life's fortunes and misfortunes: All are produced by the functions of the mind.

2

When the desire for gains burns brightly, It is nothing other than the fires of hell. When one is sunk in avarice and greed, He surely swims in a bitter sea.

But if one is determined to be pure, Raging flames become cool lake waters. And if one is determined to be enlightened, The boat will reach the other shore.

For this reason Buddha said:

When the mind changes just a little, The world quickly becomes different too. Can this not be true?

3

If one is greedy for affection, fame and status, then it is easy for him to fall into worldly snares and get burned. Only when he awakens instantly will he not sink into the sea of suffering.

Perseverance

1 A rope pulled back and forth will eventually cut through wood.

2 Water dropped bit by bit will eventually wear through stone.

3 He who studies the Way should increase his efforts in the search. Water flowing long enough will eventually make a ditch. The melon that ripens will one day drop from the vine.

4 He who obtains the Way will leave everything to Nature.

When one is studying or practising the Way, one has to be diligent. Flowing water will eventually find its course just as a ripened fruit will fall to the ground.

118

Freshness and Clarity

1

If one observes the colour of the mountains just after the rain,
He is aware that the scenery is fresh and beautiful.

2

If one hears the sound of the bell in the evening peace,
He considers its reverberations all the more high and clear.

In the midst of tranquil surroundings, there is a chance for one's original nature to manifest itself.

Loftiness of Mind

1. Climbing to high elevations makes the heart expansive.

2. Looking out on flowing waters takes one's thoughts far away.

3. Reading books on a night of snow or rain Purifies the spirit.

4. Leisurely singing some lines at the crest of a hill Makes one's inspiration soar.

Only when one opens up one's mind will he enter a higher dimension. The best way of living is to be close to what is natural.

Expansive and Narrow Mind

1 — When the mind is expansive,

2 — !

3 — Even the highest salary is like an unglazed jug.

4 — When the mind is narrow,

5 — Even a single hair resembles a wagon wheel.

6 — Get lost! Don't stand in my way.

A person with an expansive mind looks far and does not get mesmerised by superficial things before him. A petty-minded person tends to contend with others and is thus incapable of doing great things.

Transcendence

1. When one has come to an understanding of himself,

2. He can, for the first time, let the world take care of its own.

3. When one returns the world to itself,

4. He can, for the first time, transcend society — yet be right in it.

A person who recognizes that he is but one of the constituents of Nature is a person of worth. He will transcend the ways of the world and not be subject to worldly bondage.

123

Staying Within Limits

1. Viewing flowers in partial bloom,

2. Drinking wine to only slight intoxication:

3. Within such things there is a strong sense of refinement.

4. But if one goes as far as full bloom or falling down drunk, He gets into evil territory.

5. He who steps towards repletion Should think this over well.

When too ripe, a fruit will drop off. When one slackens, a deed will not be accomplished. Only when a thing is near completion will one see its potential and meaning. "Not to slacken and not to over-exert" is the way to handle worldly affairs.

Puppets on a String

1

The human being is, fundamentally, nothing more than a puppet.

2

One needs only to have his hands at the source To let no string become tangled, To pull and release each freely, To have stop or go reside in oneself,

And not to allow one thin hair to be manipulated by another. Thus he will surely transcend this place.

One step at a time.

3

How not to become a puppet controlled by others? One has to act in accord with original nature and not be influenced by external circumstances. When he is not manipulated by others, he is full of boundless freedom.

Farewell!

I can't move freely.

Good Enough

1. I do not wish for the finest tea, but the jar is never empty.

2. I do not ask for the purest wines, but the cask is never dry.

3. My plain lute is without strings, but always in tune.

4. My short flute is not hollow, but is just right for itself.

5. Though it is difficult to play as well as the Emperor Fu Xi,

6. I can count myself equal to Ji Kang and Yuan Zhi.*

As long as one knows how to derive happiness from whatever he does, he will not be particular about appearances. He takes things as they come and has peace of mind always.

*Two of the Seven Sages of the Bamboo Grove.

127

Asiapac Comic Series (by Tsai Chih Chung)

Art of War
Translated by Leong Weng Kam

The Art of War provides a compact set of principles essential for victory in battles; applicable to military strategists, in business and human relationships.

Book of Zen
Translated by Koh Kok Kiang

Zen makes the art of spontaneous living the prime concern of the human being. Tsai depicts Zen with unfettered versatility; his illustrations spans a period of more than 2,000 years.

Da Xue
Translated by Mary Ng En Tzu

The second book in the Four Books of the Confucian Classics. It sets forth the higher principles of moral science and advocates that the cultivation of the person be the first thing attended to in the process of the pacification of kingdoms.

Fantasies of the Six Dynasties
Translated by Jenny Lim

Tsai Chih Chung has creatively illustrated and annotated 19 bizarre tales of human encounters with supernatural beings which were compiled during the Six Dyansties (AD 220-589).

Lun Yu
Translated by Mary Ng En Tzu

A collection of the discourses of Confucius, his disciples and others on various topics. Several bits of choice sayings have been illustrated for readers in this book.

New Account of World Tales
Translated by Alan Chong

These 120 selected anecdotes tell the stories of emperors, princes, high officials, generals, courtiers, urbane monks and lettered gentry of a turbulent time. They afford a stark and amoral insight into human behaviour in its full spectrum of virtues and frailties and glimpses of brilliant Chinese witticisms, too.

Origins of Zen
Translated by Koh Kok Kiang

Tsai in this book traces the origins and development of Zen in China with a light-hearted touch which is very much in keeping with the Zen spirit of absolute freedom and unbounded creativity.

Records of the Historian
Translated by Tang Nguok Kiong

Adapted from Records of the Historian, one of the greatest historical work China has produced, Tsai has illustrated the life and characteristics of the Four Lords of the Warring Strates.

Roots of Wisdom
Translated by Koh Kok Kiang

One of the gems of Chinese literature, whose advocacy of a steadfast nature and a life of simplicity, goodness, quiet joy and harmony with one's fellow beings and the world at large has great relevance in an age of rapid changes.

Sayings of Confucius
Translated by Goh Beng Choo

This book features the life of Confucius, selected sayings from The Analects and some of his more prominent pupils. It captures the warm relationship between the sage and his disciples, and offers food for thought for the modern readers.

Sayings of Han Fei Zi
Translated by Alan Chong

Tsai Chih Chung retold and interpreted the basic ideas of legalism, a classical political philosophy that advocates a draconian legal code, embodying a system of liberal reward and heavy penalty as the basis of government, in his unique style.

Sayings of Lao Zi
Translated by Koh Kok Kiang & Wong Lit Khiong

The thoughts of Lao Zi, the founder of Taoism, are presented here in a light-hearted manner. It features the selected sayings from Dao De Jing.

Sayings of Lao Zi Book 2
Translated by Koh Kok Kiang

In the second book, Tsai Chih Chung has tackled some of the more abstruse passages from the Dao De Jing which he has not included in the first volume of Sayings of Lao Zi.

Sayings of Lie Zi
Translated by Koh Kok Kiang

A famous Taoist sage whose sayings deals with universal themes such as the joy of living, reconciliation with death, the limitations of human knowledge, the role of chance events.

Sayings of Mencius
Translated by Mary Ng En Tzu

This book contains stories about the life of Mencius and various excerpts from "Mencius", one of the Four Books of the Confucian Classics, which contains the philosophy of Mencius.

Sayings of Zhuang Zi
Translated by Goh Beng Choo

Zhuang Zi's non-conformist and often humorous views of life have been creatively illustrated and simply presented by Tsai Chih Chung in this book.

Sayings of Zhuang Zi Book 2
Translated by Koh Kok Kiang

Zhuang Zi's book is valued for both its philosophical insights and as a work of great literary merit. Tsai's second book on Zhuang Zi shows maturity in his unique style.

Strange Tales of Liaozhai
Translated by Tang Nguok Kiong

In this book, Tsai Chih Chung has creatively illustrated 12 stories from the Strange Tales of Liaozhai, an outstanding Chinese classic written by Pu Songling in the early Qing Dynasty.

Zhong Yong
Translated by Mary Ng En Tzu

Zhong Yong, written by Zi Si, the grandson of Confucius, gives voice to the heart of the discipline of Confucius. Tsai has presented it in a most readable manner for the modern readers to explore with great delight.